Light the Fire

Liam Lawton

Choir/People's Edition

VERITAS

First published 1996 by
Veritas Publications
7-8 Lower Abbey Street
Dublin 1

ISBN 1 85390 244 6

Light the Fire is also available as a piano/guitar score and on CD and audio cassette tape.

Cover Design: Bill Bolger
Notesetting & Typesetting: Ian Callanan OP
          Maelruain Publications, St Mary's Priory, Tallaght, Dublin 24
Printed in the Republic of Ireland by Criterion Press Ltd, Dublin
Background cover illustration: The Slide File, Dublin

table of contents

INTRODUCTION

In this collection of songs I have tried in some small way to celebrate the beautiful rich tradition of our people. As I begin to uncover the untold beauty of our Celtic heritage I feel compelled to share my song with others. It is a song that finds its roots in the stories, prayers and voices of our people calling all from North, East, South and West to gather to celebrate the Lord's presence among his people – and in gathering, we come with the spirits of our Celtic ancestors to break the word and break the bread – the unbroken tradition among a people who always remained faithful, even in the darkest hour.

In the setting of the Eucharist, I hope the spirit of joy, the spirit of hope and the spirit of wonder known to our Celtic family will prevail – even through days of darkness and the days of light. I pray that the songs will reflect the struggle of the human heart – in search of peace, in search of dignity and, above all, in search of our Creator.

Days of pain and sorrow are remembered in the song of the Famine – 'The Darkest Hour' – or in 'The Martyr's Theme'. Wonder at the God who lives within the beauty of nature and within the human heart is the theme of 'Every Heart' or 'The Hermit's Song', while hope in the journey of tomorrow is the song of Brigid, or Brendan, and all who continue to guide us. 'Light The Fire' is an anthem of hope – a song to hold sacred the flame of faith lit so many generations ago.

I hope all who sing these songs will find in their souls the heart of the Celtic experience that separates neither humanity from God nor God from humanity – a God who is never far away and who constantly enriches the world.

I am grateful to so many who have allowed 'my song' to be known – especially to Fr Sean Melody of Veritas, for making this publication possible, to Ian Callanan OP, who prepared the manuscript, to my family and friends who continue to inspire me, and, lastly, God, who has opened my soul to beauty of my Celtic tradition.

may there be no end to our singing
may there be no end to our praise
may the God of love still guide us
till His calling ends our days

Liam Lawton
Knockbeg College
Carlow

could it be?

Words and Music by
Liam Lawton

Introduction:

Verse 1, 2:

Seek the calm, the moon is shin - ing.
Seek the truth, wis - dom un - know - ing.

Div - ine its lin - ing and the wind _____ sings in
Faith ev - er grow - ing, or the heart _____ cries in

prayer. Seek his balm
vain. Love in truth.

The soul re - fin - ing spi - rits en - twin - ing for the
Deep riv - ers flow - ing, God's love ex - toll - ing for the

day of the Lord is near. So
day of the Lord is near. And

fly my soul to its sec - ret a - bode,
fly the soul to its sec - ret a - bode,

7

seek - ing some word to light - en the
seek - ing some word to light - en the

load. Could it be, could it
load. Could it be, could it

be, that God could — right the
be, that God would — hear the

wrong? ____ Could it be, could it
prayer? ____ Could it be, could it

be that God could — hear my
be, I'll find his — peace some

song?
day?

Gather

Words and Music by
Liam Lawton
Vocal Arrangement by
Ian Callanan OP

Introduction:

Verses:

V1.	Ga - ther	from	the	East,	ga	-	ther	from the West,
V2.	Ga - ther	all	the	nee - dy,	ga	-	ther	all in pain
V3.	Ga - ther	all	for - got - ten,	ga	-	ther	all for - lorn,
V4.	Ga - ther	from	all	ra - ces,	ga	-	ther	from all creeds,

ga - ther	from	the	high - ways	too.
ga - ther	all	who	cry	in	vain.
ga - ther	all	who	weep	and	mourn.
ga - ther	that	you	may	be - lieve.

Ga - ther	from	the	North,	ga - ther	from the South,
Ga - ther	all	the	thirs - ty,	ga - ther	all the poor,
Ga - ther	all	the	si - lent,	ga - ther	all who sing,
Ga - ther	all	you	ag - es,	ga - ther	in his keep,

ga - ther	when	the	night	is	noon.
ga - ther	all	in	Je - sus'	name.
ga - ther	all	the	hearts	re - born.
ga - ther	in	the	Lord's	own	peace.

Refrain:

And we'll ga - ther and we shall reap, and no long - er in sad - ness we'll weep. And we'll ga - ther, and we shall reap, And we'll

rest - ing, ris - ing, call - ing, guid - ing, O ____ Lord.

(to verses)

The Martyrs' Theme

I Rejoiced

Psalm 121

Words and Music by
Liam Lawton
Vocal Arrangement by
Ian Callanan OP and Liam Lawton

Introduction:

Refrain:

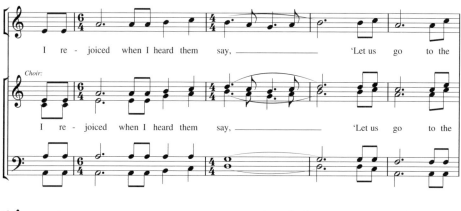

I re - joiced when I heard them say, ___ 'Let us go to the

Choir:

I re - joiced when I heard them say, ___ 'Let us go to the

house ___ of the Lord.' ___ I re - joiced when I heard them say, ___

house ___ of the Lord.' ___ I re - joiced when I heard them say, ___

Verses:

how can 1 repay?

Psalm 116

Words and Music by
Liam Lawton

Introduction:

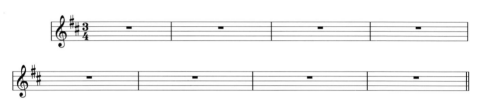

Refrain:

How can I re - pay the Lord for his good - ness to___ me?

How can I re - pay the Lord for his good - ness to__ me?

Verse 1:

I will call, I will call, on the Lord's own name, my vows to the

Lord,___ I will ful - fil. _____ I will call, I will call,

on the Lord's own name. O prec - ious in - deed, in the eyes___ of the

(to ref.)

Lord is the love of his faith - ful one.

Verse 2:

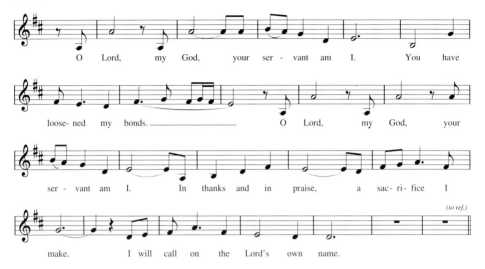

O Lord, my God, your ser - vant am I. You have loose- ned my bonds. _____ O Lord, my God, your ser - vant am I. In thanks and in praise, a sac- ri- fice I make. I will call on the Lord's own name.

(to ref.)

Verse 3:

I trust, I trust, ev- en when I say, look at me in all __ my woe. _____ I trust, I trust, in day- light I will pray, the cup of sal- va- tion my hand __ will __ raise. I will call on the Lord's own name.

(to ref.)

15

the eucharist

holy, holy

Music by
Liam Lawton

Ho - ly, ho - ly, ho - ly Lord, God of po - wer and might, hea - ven and earth____ are full of your glo - ry. Ho - san - na in____ the high - est. Ho - san - na in the high - est, Ho - san - na in the high - est, Ho - san - na in the high - est, Ho - san - na in____ the high - est. Bless - ed is he, bless - sed is

he who comes in the name of the Lord.

Bless - ed is he, bless - ed is he who comes in the

name of the Lord. _____ Ho - san - na in the

high - est. Ho - san - na in the high - est.

Ho - san - na in the high - est. Ho -

san - na in _____ the high - est.

memorial acclamation

Music by
Liam Lawton

Presider: Let us pro-claim the mys - te - ry of faith.

All: When we eat this bread, ____ when we drink this cup, ____

We pro - claim your death ____ we pro - claim your death, Lord Je - sus.

When we eat this bread, ____ when we drink this cup, ____

We pro - claim your death Lord, un - til you come in glo - ry.

Doxology/Great Amen

Music by
Liam Lawton
Vocal Arrangement by
Ian Callanan OP

Through him, with him, and in him. A - men. In the un - i - ty of the Ho - ly Spi - rit. A - men. All glo - ry and hon - our is yours, al - migh - ty Fa - ther, for e - ver and ev - er. A - men.

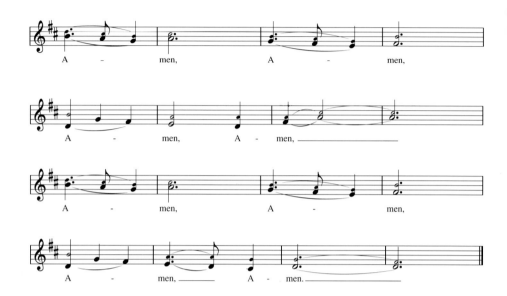

A - men, A - men,

A - men, A - men, _____

A - men, A - men,

A - men, _____ A - men. _____

every heart

Words and Music by
Liam Lawton

Introduction:

Verses:

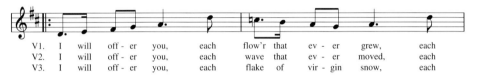

V1. I will off-er you, each flow'r that ev-er grew, each
V2. I will off-er you, each wave that ev-er moved, each
V3. I will off-er you, each flake of vir-gin snow, each

bird that ev-er flew, each wind that ev-er blew.
heart that ev-er loved, your Fa-ther's well be-loved.
spring the earth be-low, each hu-man joy and woe.

Ev'-ry thun-der roll-ing, ev'-ry church bell toll-ing.
Ev'-ry riv-er dash-ing, ev'-ry light-ning flash-ing.
Ev'-ry cloud that swept_____ o'er the skies and wept. Where

Ev'-ry leaf and sod. O
Like an An-gel's sword. O
mo-ther na-ture sings. O

Ah!_____ Ah!_____ O
Ah!_____ Ah!_____ O
Ah!_____ Ah!_____ O

21

great	and	beau - ti - ful	God.	O
great	and	beau - ti - ful	Lord.	O
great	and	beau - ti - ful	King.	O

Ah!	Ah!	O
Ah!	Ah!	O
Ah!	Ah!	O

great	and	beau - ti - ful	God.
great	and	beau - ti - ful	Lord.
great	and	beau - ti - ful	King.

(to verses 2, 3)

SONG FOR ÓRAN
GLORIA

Music by
Liam Lawton

Introduction:

Refrain:

Descant
Glo - ry to God in the high - est and

Melody Glo - ry to God in the high - est and

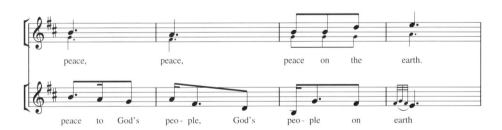

peace, peace, peace on the earth.

peace to God's peo - ple, God's peo - ple on earth

Glo - ry to God in the high - est and

Glo - ry to God in the high - est and

23

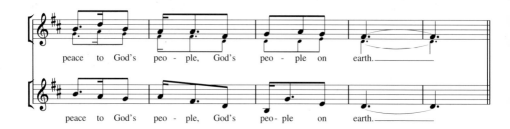

peace to God's peo - ple, God's peo - ple on earth.

peace to God's peo - ple, God's peo - ple on earth.

Verse 1:

Glo - ry to God in the high - est, _____ and

peace to God's peo - ple on earth. _____

Glo - ry to God in the high - est, and _____

(to ref.)

peace to God's peo - ple on earth. _____

Verse 2:

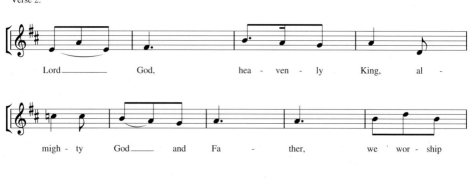

Lord _____ God, hea - ven - ly King, al -

migh - ty God _____ and Fa - ther, we wor - ship

24

you, we give you thanks, we praise

you _____ for your glo - ry. *(to ref.)*

Verse 3:

Lord _____ Je - sus Christ, _____

on - ly Son of the Fa - ther, _____

Lord _____ God, Lamb of God,

you take a - way the sin of the world, _____

_____ have mer - cy on us. _____

You are sea - ted at the right hand of the Fa - ther, _____

_____ re - ceive our prayer. _____ *(to ref.)*

25

Verse 4:

You a - lone are the Ho - ly One,

you a - lone are the Lord, _____

you ____ a - lone are the Most _____ High,

Je - sus Christ, _____

with the Ho - ly Spi - rit, _____ in the

glo - ry, the glo - ry of

(to ref.)

God the Fa - ther.

the darkest hour

Words and Music by
Liam Lawton
Vocal Arrangement by
Ian Callanan OP

Refrain:

Free Style

The dark-est hour, when land no more would flower. The dark-est hour,

when life's sweet taste was sour. Who knows the hour, the dark-est hour?

Verses:

V1. And will there be re - mem - ber - ing, for those who died
V2. And will there be re - mem - ber - ing, of skies that knew

in vain? And will there be a song to sing, to
no sun, of winds that blew thro' leaf - less trees, of

soothe the cry of pain, to green the earth a - gain? *(to ref.)*
birds that ne - ver sung? O poor for - got - ten one.

27

Verse 3:

And shall we sleep re - mem - ber - ing, the night that knew

no end? And life's sweet hope was van - ish - ing, be

cause we knew no friend. 'Twas death we did be - friend. *(to ref.)*

Pilgrim Song
Alleluia

Music by
Liam Lawton
Vocal Arrangement by
Ian Callanan OP

Introduction:

Refrain:

Al - le, ___ Al - le - lu, Al - le - lu - ia!

Al - le ___ Al - le - lu, ___ Al - le - lu - ia! ___

Al - le, ___ Al - le - lu, Al - le - lu - ia!

Al - le, ___ Al - le - lu, ___ Al - le - lu - ia! *(to verse)*

29

Verse:

Speak, O Lord, your ser - vant here is list' - ning.

You have the mes - sage of e - ter - nal life._____

Speak, O Lord, your ser - vant here is list' - ning.

(to ref.)

You have the mes - sage of e - ter - nal life.____

The Weaver

Words and Music by
Liam Lawton
Vocal Arrangement by
Ian Callanan OP

Verse 1, 2:

V1. Who will make the sun to rise?
V2. Who will thresh and grind the wheat?

Who will wash with tears, the skies?
Who will bless the bread we eat?

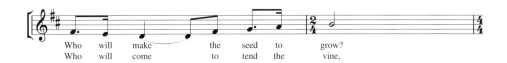

Who will make the seed to grow?
Who will come to tend the vine,

Let your cool - ing wa - ters flow,
turn the wa - ter in - to wine?

(to verse 2)

let the winds of com - fort blow.
Be for us the liv - ing sign.

Verse 3:

Melody

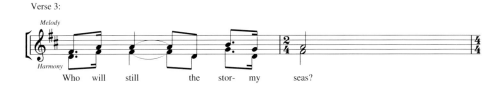

Harmony

Who will still the stor - my seas?

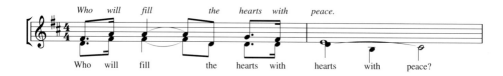

Who will fill the hearts with peace.

Who will fill the hearts with hearts with peace?

Who will put the child at ease?

When the night's des - cend - ing, _____

hear our words as - cend - ing.

Verse 4:

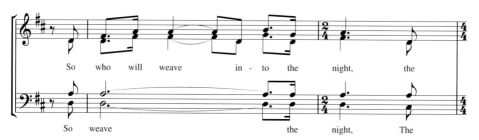

So who will weave in - to the night, the

So weave the night, The

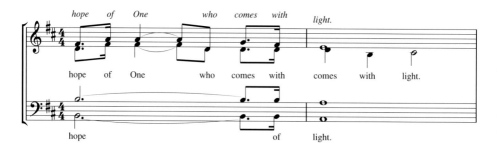

hope of One who comes with light.

hope of One who comes with comes with light.

hope of light.

Who will weave in - to this life?

Weave in - to this life.

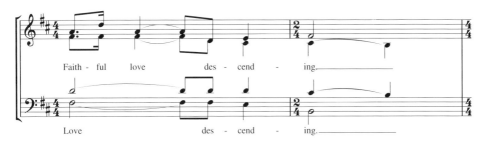

Faith - ful love des - cend - ing.

Love des - cend - ing.

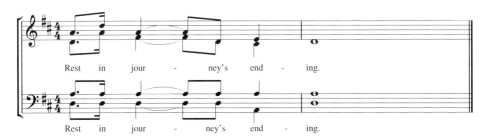

Rest in jour - ney's end - ing.

Rest in jour - ney's end - ing.

a celtic rune

Words and Music by
Liam Lawton
Vocal Arrangement by
Ian Callanan OP

kyrie

Words and Music by
Liam Lawton
Vocal Arrangement by
Ian Callanan OP

Cantor: You are Lord of all cre - a - tion: Ky - ri - e e - le - i-

son._____ *All:* Ky - ri - e e - le - i - son. Ky - ri-

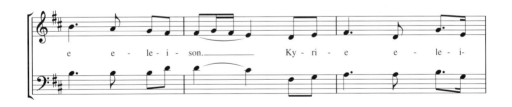

e e - le - i - son._____ Ky - ri - e e - le - i-

son. Ky - ri - e e - le - i - son._____

Cantor: You are hope, be our word, our con-so-la-tion. Chris - te e-le-i-son. All: Chris - te e-le-i-son. Chris - te e-le-i-son. Chris - te e-le-i-son. Chris - te e-le - i - son.

Cantor: You shield our steps in the light of God's sal - va - tion. Ky-ri - e e-le-i-son. All: Ky-ri - e e-le-i-son. Ky-ri -

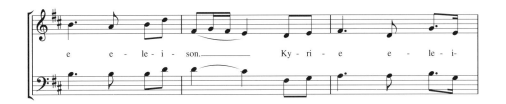

e e - le - i - son._____ Ky - ri - e e - le - i-

son. Ky - ri - e e - le - i - son._____

PATER NOSTER

Music by
Liam Lawton

peace prayer

Liam Lawton

The peace of Christ, on ev'-ry tide. The peace of
The peace of Christ, in dark and light. The peace of

Christ be by your side, The peace of Christ, on ev'-ry
Christ in day and night. The peace of Christ, be near and

shore. The peace of Christ, at ev'-ry door.
far. The peace of Christ, in ev'-ry heart.

Lamb of God, you take a-way the sin of all the

world, _____ have mer-cy on us, O Lord.

Lamb of God, you take a-way the sin of all the

world, _____ grant us your peace, grant us your

peace, grant us your peace, O Lord.

the heRmit song

Words and Music by
Liam Lawton
Vocal Arrangement by
Ian Callanan OP

Introduction:

Refrain:

Take_____ this song to share.

Take_____ this si - lent prayer.

Take_____ your rest in still of day.

So shall you know, so shall you go.

(to verses)

So shall you know, the quiet _____ call.

Verses:

1. Gen - tle his call to all who hear.
2. Swift bird ___ flies in heav - en's praise.

Gen - tle his hand _____ to
Swift swirl the clouds _____ in

all in fear. _____ Gen - tle the
o - ceans' gaze. _____ Swift flow my

wind for he is near. The
thoughts thro' end - less days. That

ri - ver falls be - fore his ___ name. *(to ref.)*
I might sing this song of ___ praise.

41

The Hermit Song

Alternative Text

Words and Music by
Liam Lawton
Vocal Arrangement by
Ian Callanan OP

Introduction: ♩ = 80

Refrain:

Take_____ my bread to share,

Take_____ my need to care.

Bring _____ my hope to all des - pair, that

I ___ might live, that I ___ might give, that

(to verses)

I ___ might live a - mong_____ you.

Verses:

1.	Dare	to	be - lieve,	I	come	for	you,
2.	Dare	to	ac - cept,	my	peace	for	you,
3.	Dare	to	be - lieve,	I	live	for	you,

the	pro - mise	of	God, _____	I
Flow	from	God's	heart, _____	my
the	Just - ice	of	God, _____	to

speak	the	Truth. _____	Dare to be -
gift	to	you. _____	Dare to be -
live	in	truth. _____	Dare to re -

lieve	I	search	for	you,	that
lieve	I	weep	for	you,	the
ceive,	my	cour - age	too,	that

(to ref.)

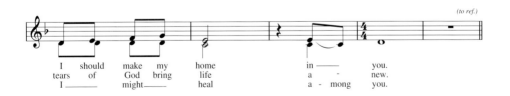

I	should	make	my	home	in ___ you.
tears	of	God	bring	life	a - new.
I ___	might ___	heal	a - mong	you.

43

for the brigidine sisters of kildare and leighlin

Light the Fire

anthem to st brigid

Words and Music by
Liam Lawton
Vocal Arrangement by
Sue Furlong

Introduction:

Verse 1:

There tra-vels forth from the pas-sag-es of his-t'ry, a wo-man's

voice, that is heard a-cross the plain. That calls once more for a peo-ple of new

vis - ion, to heal our wounds and to green our earth a -

gain, to heal our wounds and green our earth a - gain. *(to verse 2)*

Verses 2-4:

Melody.

Harmony.

V2. She spreads her cloak 'cross the land and far be - yond it, a sha-dow
V3. And wells now dry, shall ___ is - sue forth with plen - ty, to flow up-
V4. And we to - day need a pro - phet of new vis - ion. To lift the

cast | on | a | peo - ple | void | of | hope. ___ | She | speaks | of
-on | the ___ | sad | and | parch - ing | earth, ___ | to | make | a
low, | the | for - got - ten | child | to | heed. ___ | To | be | the

peace | and | the | chains | that | weigh | up - on | it, | and | there | her
prayer | from | the | hearts | now | tired | and | emp - ty, | to | call | on
voice | of | the | wound - ed | and | the | wea - ry, | to | plant | a

light | shall | glim - mer | from | the | Oak, ___ | and | all | that
her | to | bring | a - bout | new | birth. ___ | To | make | a-
-new, | a | fresh | and | peace - ful | seed. ___ | To | dance | the

binds | the | peo - ple | shall | be | broke. | *(to ref.)*
new | the | green - ing | of | the | earth.
dance | of | God's | own | bless - ed | Bríd.

Refrain:

So | light the | fire ___ | of | God's de - sire ___ | with - in | all

hearts___ let sor- rows end.___ So light the fire___ of God's de-

sire, ___ God's cho- sen one let peace on us des - cend. *(to verse 3, 4)*